Reading

How to use this book with your child:

It is recommended that an adult spends time with a child while doing any kind of school practice, to offer encouragement and guidance. Find a quiet place to work, preferably at a table, and encourage your child to hold his or her pen or pencil correctly.

Try to work at your child's pace and avoid spending too long on any one page or activity. Most of all, emphasise the fun element of what you are doing and enjoy this special and exciting time!

Don't forget to add your reward sticker to each page you complete!

Reward sticker!

Designed by Plum5

Illustrations by Sue King, Sharon Smart and Andy Geeson

Educational consultant Chris Andrew and Nina Filipek

www.autumnchildrensbooks.co.uk

Observation

Look at the picture, what can you see? Fill in the gaps below. Then write a sentence of your own describing what you see.

Dad is holding an _____

The girl is building a _____

The dog is _____

_____

_____

_____

Reward sticker!

Reading

Read the story below – it matches the picture opposite.
Can you see some of the things that happened in the picture?

Mr Jones had woken up, seen that it was a beautiful day and decided that the whole family should go to the beach. They quickly packed up everything that they thought they might need; lunch, chairs, buckets, spades, balls and towels.

When they arrived they rushed on to the beach to set up their chairs and umbrella. Mum asked if anyone was hungry, but Sophia and Billy wanted to make a sandcastle first. Billy got bored and wandered off to find crabs, but Sophia finished the sandcastle and used shells for windows and a feather on top for a flag.

Grandma decided to play with the ball, but she kicked it into the sea and Sophia had to go and get it! They had lunch, with ice creams as a treat, and Sam the dog tried to steal Dad's ice cream. Then Billy's crabs escaped from the bucket.

Reward sticker!

3

Sequencing

Read the story on page 3 again. Look at the pictures below and show in which order they happened by writing **1**, **2**, **3** or **4** in the box next to the picture.

a.

Billy got bored and wandered off to find crabs.

b.

Grandma decided to play with the ball.

c.

Sophia finished the sandcastle and used shells for windows.

d.

Sam the dog tried to steal Dad's ice cream.

Reward sticker!

Retrieval

Here are some questions based on the picture and the story. See what you can remember.

What is the boy holding? _____

Who is playing with a ball? _____

What is the girl's name? _____

Who is sleeping? _____

What colour is the girl's bucket? _____

What has she used for windows
on her sandcastle? _____

What is Sam doing? _____

Reward
sticker!

5

Inference

Now have a go at answering the questions below. You won't find the answers in the text, you will have to use the clues in the pictures and think about how you might feel if you were involved.

What might Mum say to the dog?

_____

What is the dog thinking?

_____

_____

Grandma has just kicked the ball in the sea again! How does she feel?

_____

Why might Billy be sad?

_____

_____

_____

A sleepy surprise

This story has been muddled up. Put the story in order by writing the correct letters in the boxes at the bottom of the page.

a.

Freddie called his friends over to have a look.

b.

It was a normal morning at the fire station.

c.

Suddenly, he noticed a pair of eyes staring at him.

d.

Freddie Fizz was polishing his shiny, red fire engine.

e.

But the dog was frightened and ran back to the fields.

f.

There, sitting in the door, was a dog!

1	2	3	4	5	6

Reward sticker!

What's it all about?

Look at the titles of these books. The contents of each book are written under them. Look at the questions on the next page and write your answers on the lines.

How Things Work

Contents
Safety first
Wheels at work
Rocket power
Electrifying activity
Glossary and Index

The Complete Book of Gardening

Contents
Designing your garden
The vegetable and fruit garden
Decorative garden plants
Gardening techniques
Glossary and Index

A Journey Through Time

Contents
Time chart
Early Man
The Greeks
The Romans
The Tudors
Index

The Midnight Fox

Chapters
Bad news
Abandoned
Discovery in the field
The search
Unwilling hunter
Captured
A Memory

Mountains and Valleys

Contents
The changing world
The restless earth
Mountain plants
Mountain creatures
Valley dwellers
Glossary and Index

Reward sticker!

1. In which book would you find out about The Tudors?

    _____

2. Which book is about science?

    _____

3. Which book is probably fiction? How do you know?

    _____

4. If you wanted to grow tomatoes, which book should
    you read?

    _____

5. How is the earth described in Mountains
    and Valleys?

    _____

6. Why might the fox be described as midnight?

    _____

7. Which book would you like to read most and why?

    _____

    _____

On the shelf

Encyclopedias are information books that are usually arranged in alphabetical order. Look at these encyclopedias and write which book you would look in for the subjects below. The first one has been done for you.

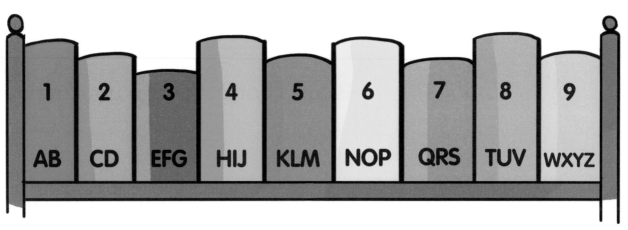

| 1 | 2 | 3 | 4 | 5 | 6 | 7 | 8 | 9 |
| AB | CD | EFG | HIJ | KLM | NOP | QRS | TUV | WXYZ |

1 antelopes

☐ fishing

☐ juggling

☐ Napoleon

☐ yaks

☐ volcanoes

☐ the Romans

☐ pirates

☐ windmills

☐ dragons

☐ Henry VIII

Can you find?

Read the passage and answer the questions below.

I was trying to find my mobile phone; it is slim, silver and has a picture of the sea on the screen. The last time I saw it, it was on the chair, but I lifted up the red cushions and it wasn't there. Next, I looked underneath the newspaper and it wasn't there either – but I did notice that Rovers had won again…and that United had lost, again. I wondered where it could possibly be? I asked my children if they had seen it, but they just looked blankly at me and shook their heads. Then Erin had a great idea. Use our home phone to ring it, she suggested. So I did – but it was set to silent. I worried that I would never find my mobile phone. I suddenly had a horrible thought. What if it was in my jeans pocket? The jeans that I had just put in the washing machine? I raced to the kitchen, and watched my jeans spinning around and around…

1.   What was lost?   _____

2.   What did it look like?   _____

3.   Where was the first place they looked?   _____

4.   What colour were the cushions?   _____

5.   Which football team had lost?   _____

6.   Who had a great idea?   _____

7.   Why didn't the idea work?   _____

8.   Where was the mobile phone?   _____

_____   Reward sticker!

Humpty Dumpty

Read the nursery rhyme and look at the pictures. Sequence the storyline by putting numbers in the boxes to show the order it all happened in.

> Humpty Dumpty sat on a wall,
>
> Humpty Dumpty had a great fall.
>
> All the King's horses and all the King's men,
>
> Couldn't put Humpty together again!

The King's men charged around the corner and rushed up to the fallen egg.

a.

b.

There was a rather large egg sat on top of a tall wall.

c.

Unfortunately, the egg was in pieces and no one could help.

d.

"Look out!" shouted someone as the large egg tumbled from the wall. Splat!

Reward sticker!

Read this news report and answer the questions below.

Yesterday at 11 o'clock in the morning, eye witnesses report having seen a large egg climb to the top of the very tall wall in Queen's Street. Lots of people tried to stop him, saying that it was just too dangerous, however, the large egg ignored them and slowly struggled to the top of the wall. It is thought that his name was Humpty Dumpty and that he had lived in Kingsville all of his life. As he reached the top, concerned onlookers asked him to come down, but he is reported to have said that the view was amazing and he was perfectly safe. As he called this out, he wobbled and waved his short arms around wildly, trying to regain his balance, but was unsuccessful. He fell to the stones below and cracked open. Will James ran for help and returned quickly with the King's men, but there was no hope. They tried hard, but no one could put Humpty back together again.

1. What time did the accident happen?

_____

2. What was the name of the street the wall was in?

_____

3. Where did Humpty live?

_____

4. Why wouldn't Humpty Dumpty come down from the wall?

_____

5. Who ran for help?

_____

6. How do you think the witnesses felt?

_____

Reward sticker!

Recipe for cupcakes

Look at the recipe below and answer the questions on the next page.

Fairy Cakes

Ingredients

- 110g butter or margarine, softened at room temperature
- 110g caster sugar
- 2 free-range eggs, lightly beaten
- 1 tsp vanilla extract
- 110g self-raising flour
- 1-2 tbsp milk

For the icing

- 300g icing sugar
- 2-3 tbsp water
- 2-3 drops of food colouring
- hundreds and thousands, or other cake decorations

Preparation method

1. Preheat the oven to 180ºC/350ºF/Gas mark 4 and line 2 x 12-hole fairy cake tins with paper cases.

2. Mix the butter and sugar together in a bowl. Beat in the eggs, a little at a time and stir in the vanilla extract.

3. Fold in the flour using a large metal spoon. Add a little milk until the mixture is a soft consistency and spoon the mixture into the paper cases until they are half full.

4. Bake in the oven for 8-10 minutes, or until golden brown on top and a skewer inserted into one of the cakes comes out clean. Set aside to cool for 10 minutes, then remove from the tin and cool on a wire rack.

5. For the icing, sift the icing sugar into a large mixing bowl and stir in enough water to create a smooth mixture. Stir in the food colouring.

6. To ice the fairy cakes, drizzle the icing over the cakes, sprinkle with decorations and set aside until the icing hardens.

Reward sticker!

1. How many eggs are needed?

_____

2. Why do you think the butter needs to be at room temperature?

_____

3. What type of flour is required?

_____

4. How many drops of food colouring is needed for the icing?

_____

5. What type of spoon should you use to fold in the flour?

6. Why does the icing need to be smooth?

_____

7. How long do you need to cook the cakes for?

Reward sticker!

How the tortoise got its shell

Read this story and answer the questions on the next page.

The king had invited all the animals to his castle for his wedding feast. Only the tortoise stayed away and the king did not understand why. The next day he asked the tortoise why it had not come to the feast with the other animals. "There's no place like home," the tortoise replied. This answer made the king so cross, he insisted that the tortoise carry its house on its back!

Moral of the story:

Many people would rather live a simple life in the comfort of their own home than live extravagantly in somebody else's.

1. What was the king celebrating?

_____

2. Which animal did not join in the celebrations?

_____

3. What did the king make the tortoise do?

_____

_____

4. Which of the following best describes this piece of writing?

   a. a poem   b. a fable   c. a nursery rhyme

5. Look at the last sentence in the passage. This is the moral of the story. What is a moral?

   a. a song   b. a lesson   c. an introduction

Reward sticker!

The Three Billy Goats Gruff

Read this story, then answer the questions on the next page.

Once there were three billy goats called Gruff. They lived in the mountains, searching for the fresh, green grass they loved to eat. On the other side of a river was the freshest, greenest grass they had ever seen. The goats trotted towards the river until they came to a bridge.

"The bridge may not be very strong," said the smallest goat. "I will go first to make sure it is safe." Under the bridge there lived a wicked, old troll. When the smallest goat's hooves went trip, trap on the wooden planks, the troll peeped over the edge of the bridge.

"Who's that trip-trapping across my bridge? I'm a troll and I'm going to eat you for my dinner!" he roared.

But the goat replied, "I'm the smallest billy goat Gruff. My brother will be tastier than me." So the troll let the smallest goat go.

Next the middle-sized goat began to cross the bridge. When he was in the middle, the wicked old troll popped up again.

"Who's that trip-trapping across my bridge?" he roared. "I'll eat you up!" But the middle-sized goat replied, "Wait for my brother. He is much bigger!" So the greedy troll let the middle-sized goat go.

The biggest goat had seen everything that had happened and smiled to himself. His big hooves went trip, trap on the wooden planks. This time the troll jumped out and stood on the bridge.

"Who's that trip-trapping on my bridge?" he shouted. "Dinner at last!"

"I'm the biggest billy goat Gruff," came the reply. He lowered his horns and CHARGED!

With a great roar, the troll flew into the air and into the river below. The water carried him away, never to be seen again, and the billy goats Gruff lived happily ever after.

Reward sticker!

1. How many goats were there?

_____

2. Where did the goats live?

_____

3. Which two words are used to describe the grass on the other side of the river?

_____

4. What sound did the goats' hooves make when they crossed the bridge?

_____

5. Find two words that describe the troll.

_____

6. Why did the troll let the smallest billy goat Gruff cross the bridge?

_____

7. 'He lowered his horns and CHARGED!' Why is the word 'CHARGED' written in capital letters?

_____

8. Which of the following describes this type of writing?

a. a diary   b. a nursery rhyme   c. a fairy tale

The Magic Porridge Pot

Read the passage below, then answer the questions on the next page.

Once upon a time there was a little girl who lived with her mother. They were very poor and had nothing to eat. One day the girl met an old woman who gave her a little pot. All she had to say was, "Cook, little pot, cook" and the pot would cook good, sweet porridge. To make it stop cooking she just had to say, "Stop, little pot, stop".

One day when the girl went for a walk, the mother felt hungry and asked the pot to cook. But the mother did not know how to stop it. Soon the porridge began to cover the kitchen and then the house. It was not long before all of the houses in the street were full of porridge.

Just as the porridge was reaching the last house in the town, the little girl came home and cried, "Stop, little pot, stop!" From that day on, anyone who wanted to come back to the town had to eat their way through the porridge.

Reward sticker!

1. The story starts with 'Once upon a time.'
   What type of story usually starts with this opening?

2. Who gave the little girl the pot?

3. Why do you think that she did this?

4. Where did the little girl go when the
   accident happened?

5. What words did the mother forget to say?

6. How did the villagers get rid of the porridge?

7. What food would you like a magic pot to make?
   Draw a picture of it in the box below.

Reward
sticker!

Pancake recipe

Look at the recipe below and answer the questions on the next page.

Ingredients

- 100g plain flour
- 2 eggs
- 300ml semi-skimmed milk
- 1 tbsp sunflower oil or vegetable oil, plus extra for frying
- a pinch of salt

Preparation method

1. Put the flour and a pinch of salt into a large mixing bowl and make a dip in the centre. Crack the eggs into the middle, then pour in about 50ml milk and 1 tbsp oil. Start whisking from the centre, gradually drawing the flour into the eggs, milk and oil. Once all the flour is mixed, beat until you have a smooth, thick paste. Add a little more milk if it is too stiff to beat.

2. To finish, add a good splash of milk and whisk to loosen the thick batter. While still whisking, pour in a steady stream of the remaining milk and stir.

3. Wipe the pan with oiled kitchen paper and then then heat the pan. Pour some batter into the pan, tilting the pan to move the mixture around for a thin and even layer.

4. When one side is cooked tilt the pan and flip the pancake.

Reward sticker!

1. How many eggs are needed?

_____

2. What type of milk is used?

_____

3. What do you first put into the bowl?

_____

4. What is the mixture called in Step 2 of the method?

_____

5. How does the recipe say to turn the pancake over?

_____

6. What do you like to eat with your pancakes?

_____

Reward
sticker!

Football fever

Answer the questions
using the picture.

1. How many players are there in the picture?

   _____

2. What colour is their kit?

   _____

3. How do you think they are feeling? Why?

   _____

4. What has just happened? How do you know?

   _____

5. How do you think the other team are feeling?

   _____

Reward
sticker!

Newspaper stories are called **articles**. Read the article below and answer the questions.

BLUES WIN AGAIN

Blues 2 – 1 Reds

The Blues won their 36th game in a row…that is a club record! Dominic Smart scored his second goal against a brave Reds' defence to make sure that the Blues' unbeaten run continued. It looked a little uncertain for a while after Edward Chapman had put the London team ahead in the 4th minute. The Reds' fans, who had travelled a long way, were singing loudly throughout the game, but went home unhappy after losing yet another game.

6. Who was the game between?

_____

7. How many games had the Blues won in a row?

_____

8. Who scored the goal for the Reds?

_____

9. Where do the Reds come from?

_____

10. Why did the Reds fans go home unhappy?

_____

Reward sticker!

The Three Wishes

Read the passage, then answer the questions opposite.

Aladdin walked nervously into the Cave of Wonders. It was amazing – as the name suggested! He looked around and saw mountains of gold, jewels that glittered like stars in the night and steps that led deeper into the cave.

He stopped, looked around and shrugged his shoulders. He knew that the only thing he was here to find was the lamp. He didn't know why. All he had been told was to find the lamp, but he had been warned not to take anything else or the cave would close and he would be trapped! He walked slowly past large piles of rubies that were bigger than his head, past chests of diamonds and chains of pearls. His eyes were set on the lamp. The lamp was placed on top of a large hill. The hill was made of silver treasures. As Aladdin walked up his feet slipped, but he was careful not to pick up any of the objects. He had been warned.

As he reached the top of the pile of silver his hand slowly reached around the lamp, his fingers curling around the precious object. Precious object? Really? It didn't look precious. It was dull and dented. But still, he picked it up and slid quickly down the silver mountain.

When he finally reached the bottom, Aladdin looked closely at the lamp. Why was this thing worth so much bother? He just couldn't understand it!

He noticed that there was some writing on the lamp, but it was so old that it could not be read clearly, so Aladdin took the edge of his ragged waistcoat and gave the lamp a polish.

BOOM! An explosion rocked the cavern. Aladdin blinked, but saw smoke curling out of the lamp; he was confused. He turned around and bumped into a short dark-haired man with bright eyes and a big smile on his face. Aladdin fell on to his bottom in surprise!

"Who are you?" he asked.

The man raised his eyebrow, took a deep breath and shouted, "Who am I? Who am I? I am the Genie of the lamp. What do they teach you in school these days?" Aladdin was confused; he had never been to school. The Genie took pity on him and smiled. "My friend, you are now my master and have three wishes. Any three wishes. Choose them wisely and I will make certain that they come true."

Aladdin shook his head and thought carefully for a while…

Reward sticker!

1. Where did Aladdin walk into?

_____

2. How do you think he felt? What makes you think that?

_____

3. What did he see in the cave?

_____

4. What was Aladdin looking for?

_____

5. What did Aladdin use to polish the lamp?

_____

6. Why didn't Aladdin take any of the other jewels
   or precious objects?

_____

7. What happened when Aladdin rubbed the lamp?

_____

8. How do you think Aladdin felt?

_____

9. If you had three wishes what would you ask for?

Reward
sticker!

_____

Alien Eggs

Fill in the missing words in the story from the word bank, or even use your own words if you think that you have better ones!

| stepped | looked | ache | light | yellow |

| smell | doing | tiptoed | hardly |

I _____ into the kitchen, it was late.

There was a strange glow from the window and I

carefully _____ out. It was dark, so

dark I could _____ see.

So I turned on the _____ .

Reward sticker!

There, in front of me, settled in the pure white snow, were some glowing eggs. They looked like ice but were blue, red and _____ .

They glowed and seemed to give off a strange _____ . I reached for the keys and turned the lock, I took hold of the door handle and _____ outside. I wished that I had put some shoes on, the cold snow made my feet _____ . I moved slowly towards the glowing eggs, steam was rising from them and I reached out my hand, slowly stretching towards them. Suddenly I heard a scream! "What are you _____ ?" It was my Mum...

What happened next?

_____

_____

_____

_____

Amazing aliens

Look at the story below, then answer the questions.

He walked towards me slowly, stumbling as he tripped over tree roots. He was waving his arms around, (all 6 of them!). I looked at him, utterly amazed. The smile on his face and kind eyes (even the third one) all seemed to say, "Hello, I just want to be your friend!"

The car behind him flashed its lights rapidly. Suddenly the car doors flapped wildly, like a duck trying to take off from a pond. The alien turned around and wailed. The sound was like a burglar alarm, loud, high-pitched and never ending! The car's lights stopped flashing and the alien continued to walk towards me.

The alien had purple skin, which glowed when light touched it and electric blue hair that reached to his waist. Why wasn't I worried? I thought about running, but decided my brother would never believe me if I didn't bring him proof or show him the alien!

1. What did the alien trip over?   _____

2. How many eyes did the alien have? _____

3. What do you think the car driver was trying to do?

   _____

   _____

4. What colour skin did the alien have?   _____

5. What kind of noise did the alien make? _____

   _____

6. Do you think the alien was friendly or not?
   Give reasons for your answer.

   _____

   _____

Finish the poem

Look at the poem and complete the missing words using the word bank below.

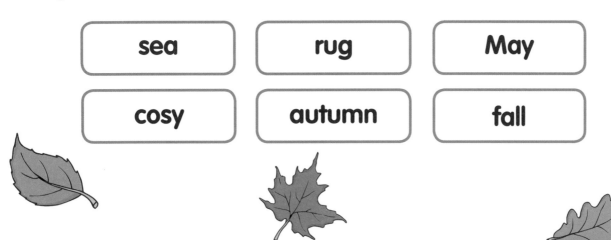

sea	rug	May
cosy	autumn	fall

I like spring when the lambs come to play,

During the months of March, April and _____.

When summer is here, we play by the _____,

My brother, my mummy, my daddy and me.

I like it in _____ when winds start to call,

A magical time when all the leaves _____.

I love winter when I'm _____ and snug,

Cuddling my puppy dog on the hearth _____.

Answers

Observation
Dad is holding an <u>ice cream</u>.
The girl is building a <u>sandcastle</u>.
The dog is <u>trying to steal the ice cream</u>.

Sequencing
a. 1, **b.** 3, **c.** 2, **d.** 4

Retrieval
The boy is holding a <u>bucket</u>.
<u>Grandma</u> is playing with the ball.
The girl's name is <u>Sophia</u>.
<u>Grandpa</u> is sleeping.
The girl's bucket is <u>blue</u>.
She has used <u>shells</u> for windows.
Sam is trying to <u>steal Dad's ice cream</u>.

A sleepy surprise
1. b, **2.** d, **3.** c, **4.** f, **5.** a, **6.** e

What's it all about?
1. A Journey Through Time.
2. How Things Work.
3. The Midnight Fox – because it has chapters and no index.
4. The Complete Book of Gardening.
5. Restless.
6. Because foxes mostly come out at night.

On the shelf
fishing **3**   the Romans **7**
juggling **4**   pirates **6**
Napoleon **6**   windmills **9**
yaks **9**   dragons **2**
volcanoes **8**   Henry VIII **4**

Can you find?
1. A mobile phone.
2. Slim, silver and had a picture of the sea.
3. The chair.
4. Red.
5. United.
6. Erin.
7. The phone was set to silent.
8. It might be in the washing machine!

Humpty Dumpty
a. 3, **b.** 1, **c.** 4, **d.** 2
1. 11 o'clock in the morning.

2. Queen's Street.
3. Kingsville.
4. Because the view was amazing and he was safe.
5. Will James.

Recipe for cupcakes
1. 2 eggs.
2. Butter is easier to mix when soft.
3. Self-raising flour.
4. 2-3 drops
5. A large metal spoon.
6. To make it easier to spread.
7. 8-10 minutes

How the tortoise got its shell
1. His wedding.
2. A tortoise
3. Carry its house on its back.
4. **b.** A fable.
5. **b.** A lesson.

The Three Billy Goats Gruff
1. 3 goats.
2. In the mountains.
3. Freshest, greenest.
4. Trip, trap.
5. Wicked, old.
6. He was greedy and wanted to eat a bigger goat.
7. To make the word stand out and give it more emphasis.
8. A fairy tale.

The Magic Porridge Pot
1. A fairy tale.
2. An old woman.
3. Because they were very poor and had nothing to eat.
4. For a walk.
5. "Stop, little pot, stop".
6. They ate their way through it.

Pancake recipe
1. 2 eggs.
2. Semi-skimmed.
3. The flour and salt.
4. Batter.
5. Flip it.

Football fever
1. 8 players.
2. Blue, red and white.
3. Happy because they have won the cup.
4. They have just won the match. We know because they are holding the cup and smiling and cheering.
5. Disappointed.
6. The Blues and The Reds.
7. 36
8. Edward Chapman.
9. London.
10. Because they had lost.

The Three Wishes
1. The Cave of Wonders.
2. Nervous – because he didn't know what was inside.
3. Mountains of gold and jewels.
4. The lamp.
5. His ragged waistcoat.
6. He had been warned not to.
7. A genie appeared.
8. Surprised.

Amazing aliens
1. Tree roots.
2. 3 eyes.
3. Scare the alien away.
4. Purple.
5. Like a burglar alarm.

Finish the poem
I like spring when the lambs come to play,
During the months of March, April and <u>May</u>.
When summer is here, we play by the <u>sea</u>,
My brother, my mummy, my daddy and me.
I like it in <u>autumn</u> when winds start to call,
A magical time when all the leaves <u>fall</u>.
I love winter when I'm <u>cosy</u> and snug,
Cuddling my puppy dog on the hearth <u>rug</u>.